In the Night Garden...™

Annual 2011

The night is black,
And the stars are bright,
And the sea is dark and deep,
And someone I know,
Is safe and snug,
And drifting off to sleep.

Round and round,
A little boat,
No bigger than your hand,
Out on the ocean,
Far away from land.

Take the little sail down,
Light the little light.
This is the way to the
Garden in the night...

Once upon a time in the Night Garden...™

Write your name and draw a picture.

....

came to play.

Who's here?

Igglepiggle
pages 8-19

Makka Pakka
pages 20-31

Upsy Daisy
pages 32-43

Tombliboos

Pontipines

Igglepiggle's accident

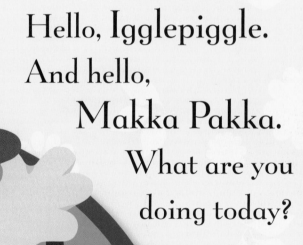

Once upon a time in the **Night Garden,** Igglepiggle came to play.

Hello, Igglepiggle. And hello, Makka Pakka. What are you doing today?

Can you count 5 stones?

Are you tidying stones Makka Pakka?
Mikka Makka Moo!
Look at that. One, two, three stones in a pile.
And five stones in a tiny circle.

What lovely, tidy stones, Makka Pakka.
Makka Pakka went home, very pleased with his **stones**.

Igglepiggle had seen
Makka Pakka's stones.
And Igglepiggle
wanted to take
a closer look.

Be careful, Igglepiggle.
Oh dear! Igglepiggle fell over.
And what do you think happened to the stones?
They were all in a mess now.
Don't worry, Igglepiggle.

Igglepiggle tried to tidy up the stones, but they didn't look right. Igglepiggle, do you think we should go and see Makka Pakka? Oh, look! Here comes the Pinky Ponk.

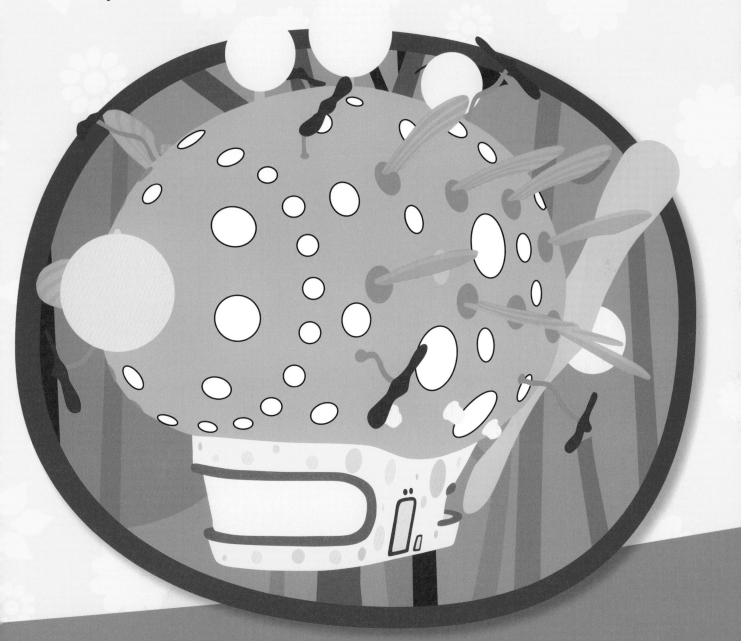

Iggle onk, tinky tonk
Flying in the Pinky Ponk.
Iggle ee and akka wakka
Going to see Makka Pakka.

The Pinky Ponk landed outside
Makka Pakka's cave.
Igglepiggle rang his bell.
And then Makka Pakka came out.

Makka Pakka!
Mikka Makka Moo!

Makka Pakka, Igglepiggle has had
an accident with your stones.
Will you come and have a look?

Makka Pakka looked over his stones.
What untidy stones!
Makka Pakka knew what to do.
And what was that?

Look at that!
Makka Pakka
has put the
stones back
just as they
were. One,
two, three
stones in a pile.
And five stones
in a tiny circle.

Makka Pakka!
Ing ang oo!

Makka Pakka is very good at tidying stones.

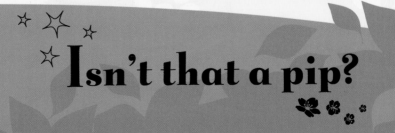

Isn't that a pip?

Yes my name is Igglepiggle!
Iggle – piggle – wiggle – niggle – diggle!
Yes my name is Igglepiggle!
Iggle – piggle – niggle – wiggle – woo!

What colour is Igglepiggle? Can you colour him in? Look at the little picture at the bottom to help you.

14

What a mess!

Oh dear. Igglepiggle loves to play, but sometimes he isn't very careful! He made Makka Pakka's stones all messy! Can you join the dots to put Makka Pakka's three stones in a pile?

Now draw stones in a little circle here. Copy the ones below if you like.

Ponk! Ponk!

Here comes the Pinky Ponk! Jump on Igglepiggle!

Ting! Ting!

Colour in this picture and then draw yourself waving to Igglepiggle from the Night Garden.

Which way?

Igglepiggle wants to go by Pinky Ponk, to Makka Pakka's house to help him put the stones right. Find a path that will take him past the Pinky Ponk and all the way to Makka Pakka.

17

Igglepiggle has arrived
at Makka Pakka's house.
Makka Pakka is in bed!
Look carefully at these three
pictures and decide which
is the odd one out.

18

Friendly fun!

Makka Pakka is helping Igglepiggle tidy the stones again.

Here is Makka Pakka's and Igglepiggle's tidy pile of stones. Can you add a stone to complete the circle of stones? Now colour your picture.

Makka Pakka's present

Once upon a time in the Night Garden,
Makka Pakka came to play.

Makka Pakka was
counting his stones.
One, two, three...
four, five, six.
Look at that – a pile of six stones.

Upsy Daaaiisy. Ooo-ooo!

Look Upsy Daisy –
Makka Pakka has made
a pile of six stones.

Makka Pakka! Toot! Toot!
What do you think
Makka Pakka did next?

Makka Pakka
gave a stone to Upsy Daisy.
A present for Upsy Daisy!
What a lovely present.

Thank you,
Makka Pakka.
Makka Pakka! Upsy Daaaisy!

One, two, three, four, five.
Five stones left.

Can you find **1, 2, 3, 4, 5** stones
on this page? Colour them in.

Look, Igglepiggle.
Makka Pakka has made
a pile of stones.
One, two, three, four, five.
Five stones.

What do you think
Makka Pakka did next?

Makka Pakka gave a stone to Igglepiggle.
Don't worry Igglepiggle, it's only a present...

What a lovely present.
Thank you, Makka Pakka.

One, two, three, four.
Four stones left.

Look Tombliboos.
Makka Pakka has made a pile of stones.
One, two, three, four.
Four stones.

A present for Tombliboo Unn,
a present for Tombliboo Ooo...
and a present for Tombliboo Eee!

Tombliboo Unn

Tombliboo Ooo

Tombliboo Eee

What lovely presents!
Thank you, Makka Pakka.

Makka Pakka has given all his

stones away – except one.
Who is that stone for?
Can you guess?

**Count the Tombliboos.
How many can you see?**

Makka Pakka had six stones.
One, two, three, four, five, six.
He gave one to Upsy Daisy.
One to Igglepiggle...
and one, two, three – to the Tombliboos.

One stone left. What a lovely
present, for Makka Pakka!

Isn't that a pip?

Makka Pakka!

Makka Pakka,
Akka wakka,
Mikka makka moo!

Hum dum,
Agga pang,
Ing ang ooo!

Makka Pakka,
Appa yakka,
Ikka akka ooo!

Makka Pakka,
Akka wakka,
Mikka makka moo!

Makka Pakka is very happy to have so many friends. Colour Igglepiggle so they can play together.

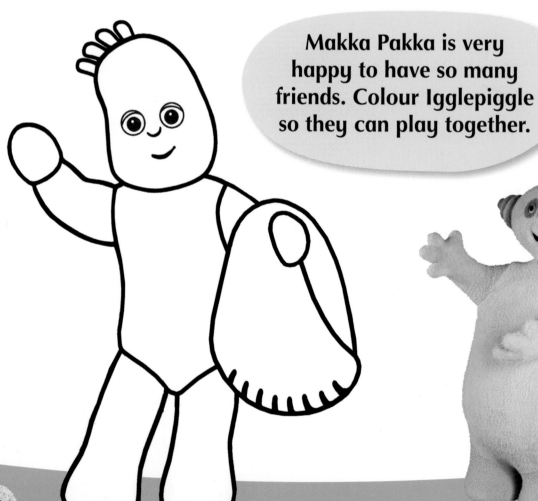

Counting time

Hello, Makka Pakka!

Parp! Parp!

Makka Pakka has six stones. Can you count six trumpets on this page? Draw a circle around each one.

Makka Pakka loves his trumpet!

Follow the path

How kind you are Makka Pakka! Makka Pakka gives a stone to each friend. Follow the path leading from each stone to see where they lead!

One stone left, for Makka Pakka! Isn't that a pip?

28

Just for you

If you could give your friends something lovely, what would you give them? Draw it here.

Night, night ...

Makka Pakka is very tired now.
Giving away stones makes Makka Pakka sleepy.

Colour this picture of him in his little bed.

What do you think
Makka Pakka is dreaming about?
Draw it in the space above.
Join the dots together around
each bubble, and then
colour them too!

Upsy Daisy and Tombliboo Eee

Once upon a time in the
Night Garden,
Upsy Daisy came to play.

Upsy Daaiisy!
What was Upsy Daisy doing?
Can you guess?
Upsy Daisy was singing a
lovely song.
La-la-la...
What a lovely song,
Upsy Daisy. Daisy Doo!

Tombliboo!
Tombliboo!
Hello, Tombliboos.
What were the
Tombliboos doing?
Can you guess?

The Tombliboos were going out,
to play in the garden.
Off they went.

First, Tombliboo Unn.

And then, Tombliboo Ooo...

33

Wait a minute, Tombliboos!
Tombliboo Eee didn't see where
the other Tombliboos went!
Are you lost, Tombliboo Eee?

Tombliboo Eee called
nice and loud, so
Tombliboo Unn and
Tombliboo Ooo
could hear her.

Tombliboo!

She called as loud as she could.

Tombliboo!
Tombliboo!

But still the other
Tombliboos couldn't hear her.
Poor Tombliboo Eee.
What are we going to do?

**Colour in the Tombliboo bush. Can you see
Tombliboo Unn and Tombliboo Ooo?**

Oh! Upsy Daisy has had a very good idea. Perhaps Tombliboo Eee can try calling loudly through Upsy Daisy's megaphone!

Daisy Doo!

So Tombliboo Eee called as loud as she could, through Upsy Daisy's megaphone.

Tombliboo!

What a very loud call! Daisy Doo!

What happened next –
can you guess?
Tombliboo! Tombliboo!
Tombliboo Unn and
Tombliboo Ooo came
back, of course.

Tombliboo Eee was lost. But her very good
friend, Upsy Daisy, had a good idea.

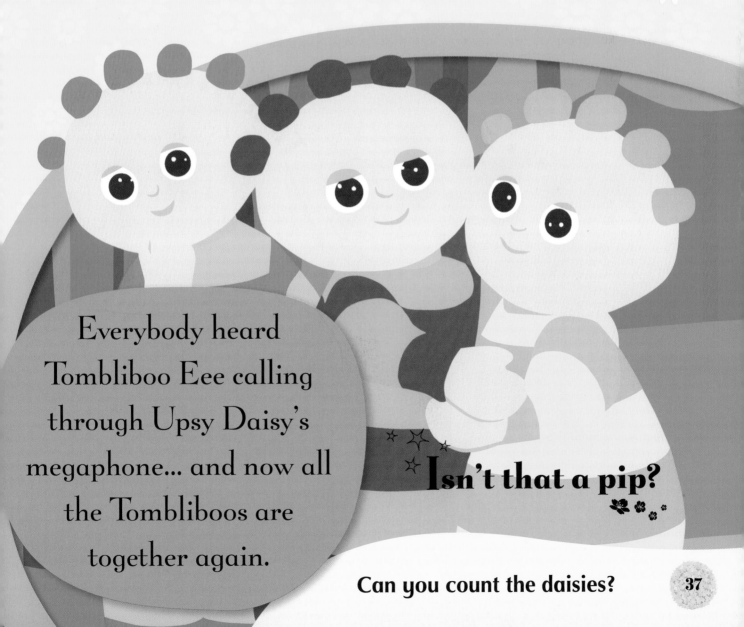

Everybody heard
Tombliboo Eee calling
through Upsy Daisy's
megaphone... and now all
the Tombliboos are
together again.

Isn't that a pip?

Can you count the daisies?

What did you say, Upsy Daisy?

Upsy Daisy's megaphone is not just for singing loudly. Upsy Daisy can help her friend Tombliboo Eee. Colour in Upsy Daisy's megaphone.

Upsy Daisy,
Here I come!
I'm the only Upsy one!
I'm the only Daisy too!
Ipsy-Upsy-Daisy-doo!

Tombliboo!

Help shout, 'Tombliboo!' for Tombliboo Eee.

Tombliboo! Tombliboo!

Draw a line connecting Tombliboo Eee to Tombliboo Unn and Tombliboo Ooo. She can't get lost again now!

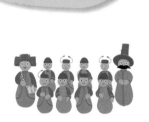

39

Hellooo!

Upsy Daisy...
Upsy Daiiisssssyyy...

Here is Upsy Daisy with her megaphone. She wants to help her friends, the Tombliboos. She is calling out and walking all around. Follow the paths that she takes with your finger. Can you find a path that will take her past three flowers?

Time for bed

Everyone is so tired now and it's time for bed. Here are four lovely pictures of Upsy Daisy in her bed. Can you spot which is the odd one out?

Ssshhhh!

Friends together

It's good to have a friend or two

Upsy Daisy has been a good friend today. She helped the Tombliboos, and they want to thank her. Colour the picture to see what the Tombliboos have brought Upsy Daisy.

Too loud, Tombliboos!

Once upon a
time in the **Night Garden**,
the Tombliboos came to play.

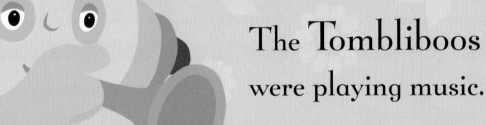

Toot! Toot!

The Tombliboos
were playing music.

Plink! Plonk!
Plinketty-plonk!
Tinkle! Tinkle!

It's very loud music, Tombliboos...

Makka Pakka! Toot! Toot!

What loud music!

The Tombliboos were playing their piano
and drums so loudly, they couldn't
hear Makka Pakka's trumpet.

Colour in the lovely Tombliboo music.

Plink! Plonk!

Plinketty-plonk! Tinkle! Tinkle!

They were playing their music so loudly, they couldn't hear Igglepiggle's bell.

Plink! Plonk!

Plinketty-plonk!   Tinkle! Tinkle!

Upsy Daisy!
Upsy Daaaaaaiiiiiisy!

The Tombliboos kept playing. They couldn't hear Upsy Daisy calling – even with her megaphone.

Plink! Plonk!
Plinketty-plonk!

Tinkle! Tinkle!
Mi-mi-mi-mi-mi-mi-mi-mi!

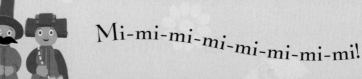

The Tombliboos carried on, playing their music. It was so loud, they couldn't hear the Pontipines calling.

But where are the Pontipine children?
And what are they doing?

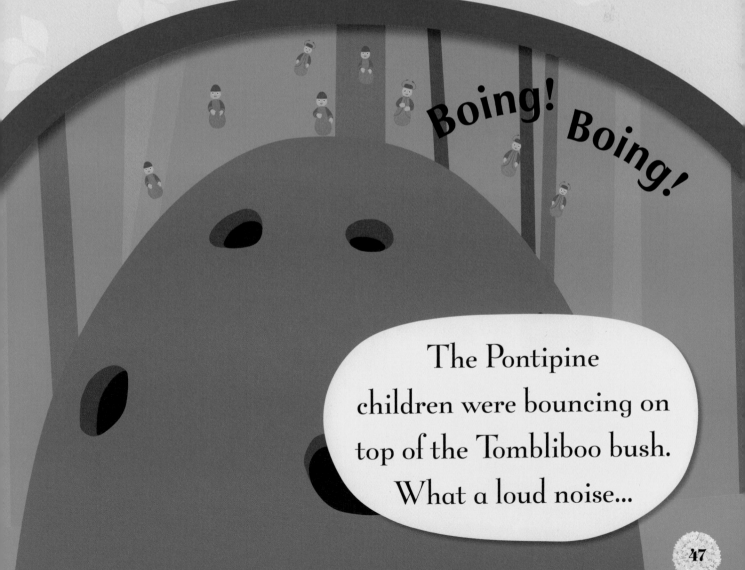

Boing! Boing!

The Pontipine children were bouncing on top of the Tombliboo bush. What a loud noise...

Boing! Boing! Boing!

What a great big noise it was.
The Tombliboos could hear that!
Plink! Plonk!
Plinketty-plonk!
Tinkle!
Tinkle!

And then everybody joined in.

That was better.
What lovely music –
and everybody joined in.

Point to all the orange music notes.

Isn't that a pip?

49

Who's here?
The Tombliboos

Ombliboo, Tombliboo,
knock on the door.
Ombliboo, Tombliboo,
sit on the floor.

Ombliboo, Tombliboo,
here is my nose,
Ombliboo, Tombliboo,
that's how it goes.

There you are!

Ombliboo, Tombliboo!

The Tombliboos are all together again at last. Can you point to:

A Tombliboo with pink spots?

A Tombliboo with pink hair?

A Tombliboo with green spots?

Which is your favourite Tombliboo?

51

Let's play!

Everybody in the Night Garden loves to play music. Today they are playing some beautiful tunes. Draw a line to connect these friends to their favourite instruments.

Not everybody in the story was playing an instrument. Who was talking into a megaphone?

52

Friends all around

Hello!
Here are all the friends from the story.

Wave hello, and colour the picture.

54

Can you

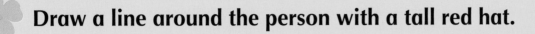

🌸 Draw a line around the person with a tall red hat.

🌸 Point to the person with the stripey tights.

🌸 Blow a kiss to your favourite!

🌸 Draw a line between two characters that look the same.

The Pontipines' ride on the Ninky Nonk

Once upon a time in
the **Night Garden**,
the Pontipines came to play.

The Pontipines are friends of mine,
Although they're only small,
And even when there's ten of them,
They're hardly there at all!

Mii-mi-mi-mi-mi-mi-mi-mi!

Pontipines, are you going
to ride on the Ninky Nonk?
Quick Pontipines – catch the Ninky Nonk!

All aboard the Ninky Nonk!
Tombliboo! Tombliboo!
But the Tombliboos got on the Ninky Nonk.

And the Pontipines were left behind.

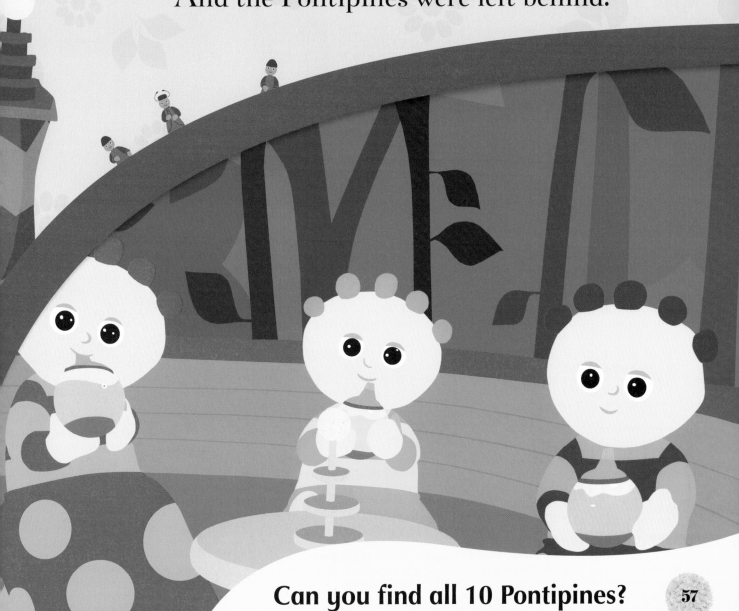

Can you find all 10 Pontipines?

57

The Ninky Nonk stopped. And there was Makka Pakka. Makka Pakka!

All aboard the Ninky Nonk!
Mi-mi-mi-mi-mi-mi-mi!
Quick Pontipines –
catch the Ninky Nonk!
Mikka Makka Moo!
Oh dear, look at that.
Makka Pakka got
on the Ninky Nonk.

But the Ninky Nonk
has gone without
the Pontipines again.

The Ninky Nonk
stopped again.
And there was
Upsy Daisy
with Igglepiggle.

All aboard the Ninky Nonk!
Upsy Daisy! Ooo!
Quick Pontipines – catch the
Ninky Nonk!
Oh dear, look at that. Upsy Daisy
and Igglepiggle got on
the Ninky Nonk.

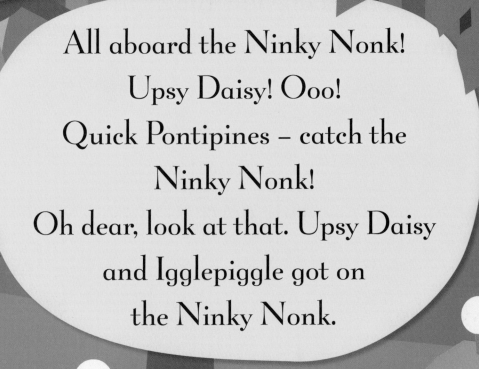

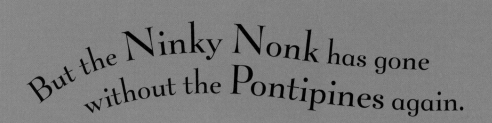

But the Ninky Nonk has gone
without the Pontipines again.

**Point to the biggest carriage
on the page.**

The Ninky Nonk stopped one last time.
And why do you think the Ninky Nonk stopped?

To pick up the teeny tiny Pontipines,
of course. At last, the Pontipines were
going to ride on the Ninky Nonk
too. And it was a very bouncy ride.

Isn't that a pip?

All aboard!

Here are lots of favourite things from the Night Garden. Look closely at the shapes and then connect each shadow with its matching picture.